Project Omega

ELAINE O'REILLY

Level 2

Series Editors: Andy Hopkins and Jocelyn Potter

O'reilly, Elain   اورایلی، ایلین
(پراجکت امگا).-
Project Omega level 2/ Elain O'reilly.-
۱۳۸۰ = ۲۰۰۱ ,جنکل :اصفهان
penguin   (   )‏.—.(رنگی) مصور :.ص [۲۵] ، ۷
(readers series; level 2

انگلیسی.
فهرستنویسی بر اساس اطلاعات فیپا .
افست از روی چاپ ۲۰۰۰: هارلو.
۱.زبان انگلیسی -- کتابهای قرائت
(دانشگاهی). ۲.زبان انگلیسی -- راهنمای آموزشی
(عالی).   الف.عنوان: Project Omega

۴۲۸/۶۴   PE۱۱۲۱/الف۸عپ
الف.۱۳۸

۸۰-۲۱۶۹۹م   کتابخانه‌ملی‌ایران
محل نکهداری :

شناسنامه کتاب:

نام کتاب: project omega
مؤلف: LAINE OREILLY
تیراژ :   ۵۰۰۰ جلد
تاریخ و نوبت چاپ: سوم – تابستان ۸۲
لیتوگرافی: گلبن
چاپ: عرفان
صحافی: نوید
ناشر :   انتشارات جنگل
021-6921166-6926639
0311-2212047-09113197507

Pearson Education Limited
Edinburgh Gate, Harlow,
Essex CM20 2JE, England
and Associated Companies throughout the world.

ISBN 0 582 42754 1

This edition first published 2000

NEW EDITION

Copyright © Penguin Books Ltd 2000
Illustrations by Mike Brownlow
Cover design by Bender Richardson White

Typeset by Bender Richardson White
Set in 11/14pt Bembo
Printed and bound in Denmark by Norhaven A/S, Viborg

Published by Pearson Education Limited in association with
Penguin Books Ltd, both companies being subsidiaries of Pearson Plc

For a complete list of the titles available in the Penguin Readers series please write to your local
Pearson Education office or to: Marketing Department, Penguin Longman Publishing,
5 Bentinck Street, London W1M 5RN.

Contents

Contents

Introduction

'I believe that the power of good is stronger than the power of evil.'

Why does Charles Hatfield Baker III, one of the richest men in New York City, suddenly disappear? His daughter wants to know. What are the directors of his company doing? And what is Project Omega? The directors want power and money, and they are not afraid of danger. They have a plan.

Julia learns about the plan after her father disappears. She learns other things, too. She learns about New York and its people, and she learns about friends. She is only eighteen, but she understands the power of money. She wants to find her father and she wants to use his money well. But can she?

Elaine O'Reilly was born in South Africa. She now has a bookshop in Rome, and she writes for children's television. She has two dogs, three cats and a daughter.

Chapter 1   A Rich Man Disappears

Charles Hatfield Baker III was a very rich man. There wasn't a richer man in New York City. He was the boss of a large number of important companies. He owned very large gardens and houses in the country. He had boats and horses and an aeroplane. But he was a nice man. He liked the everyday things of life: a good cup of coffee, a smile from a pretty girl, a walk through the park on a fine autumn day.

He had all these things on this Wednesday morning. He drank two cups of very good Italian coffee for breakfast. His daughter, Julia, smiled and said, 'Goodbye. Have a nice day, Dad.' And he left his flat for the walk to his office. He always walked through Central Park to his office on Columbus Street. He went in the lift down forty floors to the street door.

'Good morning, Mr Baker,' said Angelo, the doorman. 'Have a good day.'

'Thank you, Angelo. You too,' he answered. 'See you this evening.'

But Angelo didn't see him that evening. He never saw him again. Because Mr Baker never arrived at his office. Between Central Park and the offices of Hatfield International, Charles Hatfield Baker III disappeared.

The police tried to find him. They looked everywhere for him in the park. They started early in the morning and finished late at night. But there was nothing. They couldn't find anything.

They gave three big police dogs his old blue shirt. The dogs' noses were very busy for a minute or two, then they ran across the street to Central Park. But inside the park, they stopped. They ran up and down, up and down, this way and that way. Again, nothing.

Detectives went to the airports, to the train stations and to the bus stations. They showed photographs. 'Did you see this man last week? A tall man with white hair in expensive grey trousers and a jacket. Did he come through here last Wednesday or Thursday?'

'No,' everybody said. 'I don't remember that man.'

The detectives questioned Julia, the grey men at the office, the office workers and the doormen. They asked again and again, 'Where do you think Mr Baker is? Why did he disappear? Perhaps he *wanted* to disappear! Why?'

The answer was always: 'I don't know. I don't understand. I can't tell you.'

There were telephone calls between the FBI★ and Scotland Yard★. In the end, everybody said, 'Kidnappers! That's the answer. Charles Hatfield Baker III is a very rich man, you know. They kidnapped him for money.'

They waited and waited for a letter or a telephone call.

'The kidnappers will ask for a lot of money,' they said.

Nothing came. Not a word.

The newspapers said, 'Somebody knows something about Mr Baker. We'll give them $10,000 when they call us.'

Nothing happened.

Julia sat near the telephone every day and every night. She never went outside. She didn't cry, because she really never cried. But she got thinner and thinner. Her eyes were red because she didn't sleep. She loved her father.

'I know he isn't dead,' she thought. 'Is he trying to tell me something? But what? What does he want me to do?'

★ FBI, Scotland Yard: American and British detectives.

4

Chapter 2   The New Boss

For days, and then weeks, Julia hoped for a telephone call about her father, but nothing came. After a time, the newspapers were tired of the story. Their writers wrote about other things. The police stopped asking questions.

The months came and went. Julia saw the first snow of winter through the windows of her twelve-room flat. In one hour, Manhattan was white with snow – white and quiet. Was this really New York, or a village in the mountains?

'But it's New York,' she thought. 'It's not usually quiet. This is strange. I know New York. It's my home.'

Julia was eighteen years old. Her life was the life of a rich man's daughter. She went to the best schools. She could speak French and Spanish. She could dance and play music. She bought her clothes from the best shops, and she ate chocolate cake in expensive cafés. She drove through the city streets in big, expensive cars.

But Julia really knew nothing about New York. She knew nothing about the lives of other New Yorkers.

She saw her face in the window. She was a tall girl with dark hair and green eyes. Her face was nice but not pretty – it was a very strong face.

'Listen,' she said to her face in the window. 'You know that your father isn't coming back. Why are you sitting here and waiting? Who's going to help you? You're the boss now. I think he's telling you that. You are Julia Ann Hatfield Baker – the first!'

She put on her coat and her hat and went out in her very expensive clothes.

For the next three hours, Julia went through many of the streets of New York for the first time. She didn't drive in her father's cars. She took taxis and she walked. She looked at buildings and she looked at people. She looked into windows, and she saw people in their cold rooms. She looked at women in the streets. Their faces told her about the hungry children in their homes. She looked at men – men without jobs and without hope.

She saw this and she slowly understood.

'I know now,' she thought. 'I know that I can use my father's money well.'

Next morning, she arrived at the offices of Hatfield International at nine o'clock.

'I want to see the directors of the company at ten o'clock,' she said to Miss Bentley, in her father's office.

At ten, she looked at the five grey men round the large table in the meeting room.

'I know these men,' she thought. 'I pulled their noses when I was a baby. I danced with them at Christmas when I was a little girl. Yes, I know them. Or do I? Perhaps they think that they know *me*. They're going to be surprised.'

She looked at them again. Their faces told her nothing.

'Good morning,' she said. 'I called this meeting. Perhaps you were surprised.'

'Yes,' they said. They *were* surprised – very surprised.

'You know that my father gave me more than half of the company.'

They knew, but they weren't very happy about that.

'I want to make some changes. But first, I would like to see the company files. I want to know about the company, our money and – very important – our plans for the future.'

The eyes of the grey men met.

'Of course, my dear,' said one man.

'No problem,' said another man.

'But why?' they wanted to know. 'What changes does she want? Why does she want to know our plans for the future? What does she know about Hatfield International?'

Chapter 3   Power

For two days, Julia looked at pages of numbers and read about her father's company. The numbers were very large, and the files were thick and heavy.

Julia learnt a lot of new things about the company. Hatfield International owned places everywhere: in Texas, Australia, Africa, the Arctic, Canada . . . Hatfield International had power – a lot of power.

'This power,' she thought, 'can change people's lives in wonderful ways. It can give them jobs, hospitals, schools, teachers. But it can also do other things – bad things. And sometimes Hatfield International uses this power because it wants more power.'

This was her father's great company, and his father's company, and *his* father's company.

'And now I have to be the new boss,' Julia thought.

Julia's mother died when Julia was only a baby. She didn't remember her, but she had old photographs of her. Julia had her mother's dark hair and green eyes.

She was also her father's daughter. Julia understood money. Some people understand music, or sport, or dance. These things are easy for them. For Julia, money was easy. After two days with the files of Hatfield International, she knew a lot of things about the company. They were two very interesting days for her.

Outside, it got colder and colder. Inside the Hatfield building, Julia sat and read – words and numbers, words and numbers. People came and went, but she saw only the papers in front of her.

Late in the afternoon of the second day, she looked at the last file on the table. It was a red file. The files were all different colours. Red files were about future plans – projects for the future.

On this red file, Julia read: PROJECT OMEGA.

She opened it. There were no papers in it – only one word on the inside of the file: 'Never!'

It was her father's writing. She put the telephone to her ear. After a minute, somebody answered. Julia said, 'Miss Bentley?'

'Miss Bentley went home. Everybody went home. Can I help you?' The speaker was a girl.

'I'm looking for the papers about Project Omega.'

For a minute the girl said nothing. Then she said, 'I – I'm sorry, I don't know anything about it.'

'I don't believe her,' thought Julia. 'The girl is afraid of something.'

Julia put down the telephone. She walked to Miss Bentley's office.

A girl stood near the telephone there. She was about Julia's age, small and pretty. She *was* afraid. Julia could see that.

'I want to see the papers about Project Omega,' Julia said.

'I'm sorry, Miss Baker. I don't know anything about it – really I don't.'

Julia saw something in the girl's eyes. And when the girl spoke, she heard more than the words. There was something in the girl's eyes and in her words – between the words. Was her father trying to tell her something about Project Omega when he disappeared?

'Am I wrong about the word "Never!" and the eyes and words of this girl?' she thought. 'No! I'm *not* wrong.'

Chapter 4   Danger

Julia stood and looked at the girl. Suddenly, she felt very tired.

'It's not important,' she said. She felt sorry for the unhappy girl. 'Perhaps those papers are from an old file.'

'Is something wrong, Julia?' It was Mr Berger. He was one of the grey men, a director of her father's company. 'Did I hear you say "Project Omega"?'

Julia turned. 'When did he come into the room?' she thought.

'Yes, Mr Berger. I wanted to see the papers from the Project Omega file.'

'Did you really, Julia?' He laughed – a strange laugh, Julia thought. He had the smile of a kind uncle – of Father Christmas – but his eyes were cold. He said, 'Why are you worrying about Hatfield's problems, my dear? Do you want money? You only have to ask. You're Charlie Baker's daughter.'

Julia was very angry, but she spoke quietly.

'I'm not only Charles Baker's daughter, Mr Berger. I own more than half of Hatfield International. And now I have to tell you, I want to see those papers!'

'Of course, my dear.' He turned to the girl and said, 'Miss Harper, please get the papers for Miss Baker. They're in the safe.'

Miss Harper said nothing, but she went to one wall of the office. There was a large picture there of Charles Baker's grandfather. Miss Harper moved the picture. Behind it, there was a small, very strong door. Her fingers worked quickly. They found the right numbers and the safe opened.

'Here you are, Miss Baker,' she said. She didn't look at Julia. She turned back and closed the safe. Then she moved the picture back.

Julia took the papers and put them in her bag. Then, she left the office. Before the lift door closed, she heard Mr Berger. He started to shout at Miss Harper.

Julia went home in a taxi.

The flat was warm and quiet. She sat down in her father's chair and opened her bag.

'No,' she thought. 'I'll have some food first.'

She put the file on the floor and went into the kitchen. There was some food on the kitchen table for her. Usually she didn't eat very much, but tonight she was hungry. There were some nice vegetables, some meat and some fruit. The meat and vegetables were cold, of course, but very good. And it was her first good food for nearly two days.

She didn't take the food into the living room, but sat down at the kitchen table. Then she heard the telephone. There was a telephone in the kitchen and she went to it.

'Yes?' she said.

'Julia – I mean Miss Baker?' It was the girl from the office. Miss Harper. 'Please don't be angry with me. I had to call you. Please listen to me. You're in great danger.'

'Miss Harper? Is that you? What do you mean?'

'They don't want you to know about Project Omega. I think they – they're going to – I think they're going to kill you! Please, you have to believe me!'

'But who? Who wants to kill me? – Miss Harper? Are you there?'

No sound came from the telephone. Julia sat with the telephone in a cold hand. She heard nothing. It was quiet – and that meant danger.

'What's happening?' she thought. 'What's happening to Miss Harper? Does Project Omega mean danger for her too?'

Chapter 5   An Evil Plan

Julia put the telephone down. For the first time, she felt very lonely. She wasn't afraid, but she was lonely.

'I'm never lonely,' she thought. 'Alone sometimes, yes. But not lonely. Not without a friend in a time of problems or danger. I don't really know about danger. What does the word "danger" mean? I was always safe with my father.'

She thought about Miss Harper.

'They're going to kill me – Who are "they"? Did "they" kill my father? What is Project Omega? And why don't "they" want me to know about it?'

She went back to the living room. The file of papers was on the floor. She sat down and started to read.

She read to the end, and then she closed the file. She was very worried.

'It's very bad!' she thought. 'Very bad!'

Project Omega was the directors' plan. They planned to make a lot of money – a *lot* of money. First, Hatfield International had to buy more power than every other company – more power than most countries. But it was the plan of very bad men, men without feelings. There was only one word for it: evil. It was a really evil plan.

'They' were the directors of her father's company, and she had to stop them.

In the beginning – only the day before yesterday – Julia had a plan for her father's money. She wanted to help people in New York. She wanted to give them better homes, more jobs, a happier life.

'I went to Hatfield's offices for that,' she thought. 'I never wanted to find this. What do I have to do? How can I stop it? I have to tell the police – and the newspapers. I have to tell the world about Project Omega. Yes, tell the world. That – and only that – will stop it. I have to do that – in the morning.'

Julia went to bed. For the first time, she dreamed about her father. They were in a small boat in bad weather. They were in great danger. But he put his arms round her.

'It's all right,' he said in her dream. 'I'm here. Don't be afraid. We can't be afraid. We have to be strong.'

When Julia woke up, she felt strong. She remembered her dream.

'Perhaps Dad is dead,' she thought, 'but he's with me. I believe that the power of good is stronger than the power of evil. In my dream Dad said, "We can't be afraid." So that's all right.'

Julia wasn't afraid – not now.

She heard Clara in the kitchen. Clara cleaned and cooked for her. She was a mother to her, and Julia loved her.

Julia walked into the kitchen.

'Good morning, Clara.'

'Morning, Miss Julia. Your coffee is ready. It's cold outside – very cold. You'll be surprised. Only a week before Christmas! You're not going to stay here for the holiday, I hope. Not alone! A young girl has to have friends of her age.'

'Dear Clara. She's worried about me,' Julia thought. She said,

14

'I'll think about Christmas later, Clara. This morning, I have to do something – and it can't wait.'

She dressed very quickly. Then she put the Omega file in her bag and ran out.

She opened the door of the lift – 'No!' There was no lift there. Only cold, black nothing. The ground was forty floors below her. She started to fall.

Chapter 6　A Friend

Julia didn't fall. Two strong arms pulled her back from the dark – back to life.

For a minute, she stayed there on the floor outside her flat. She didn't feel well, but she was safe. She could see only a green jacket.

'Thank you,' she said to the green jacket.

The man in the green jacket helped her and she stood up.

'No problem. I play a lot of football, so I can move fast. But I don't usually move as fast as that.'

He was young, perhaps about twenty-five. His face was friendly.

'My name's Julia Baker. You saved my life.'

'Oh, I save lives when I can,' laughed the young man. 'I'm Edward West.'

'Thank you, Edward. Would you like to come in and have some coffee?' Julia asked. 'I'd really like a cup of coffee after that.'

They went into the flat. Clara brought them two cups of coffee – very good Italian coffee.

'The lift,' Julia said. 'It wasn't there.'

'I know.'

'But *you* were there.
That was good.'

Edward looked at her.

'Yes,' he said slowly. 'It was.'

'Was it an accident? What do you think?'

'No, I don't think it was an accident.'

'I think they broke the lift door.'

'Yes, they did.'

Julia drank the hot, black coffee. When she put the cup down, she started to cry. For the first time in her eighteen years of life, she wanted a friend. She knew it because she was with this young man – this young man with the friendly eyes.

'It's all right,' he said. 'You're safe now.'

'No, I'm not,' Julia answered. 'I'm in great danger.' And she told him the story about her father, and then Miss Harper's telephone call. She told him about Project Omega. 'And now the lift – so I really am in danger.'

He said again, 'It's all right.' And, 'I'm here now.' Her father's words in her dream. 'I can help you. There are two of us now. We'll show the world the Omega file. We'll take it to the newspapers – to the *New York Times*. I've got some friends there. We'll stop this evil plan. Don't worry.'

Julia now had a friend. He wanted to help her. She was very happy.

'Yes,' she said. 'We'll take the file to the newspaper. I'll get my bag. It has the Omega papers in it.'

But where was the bag? It wasn't in the flat. It wasn't between the flat and the lift. She looked for it. Clara looked for it.

'It isn't here,' Julia told Edward. 'And now I don't have anything for the newspapers. Who will believe that Project Omega is so evil? They won't believe it without the papers.'

Chapter 7   Happy Christmas!

'What are we going to do?' Julia asked. She was happy – very happy – because she could say 'we'.

'We have to get another copy of the file,' Edward answered.

'Of course. But how? I don't want to go back to Hatfield and ask for one. Wait . . . Miss Harper!'

'Can she get us a copy?'

'She's our only hope.'

Julia went to the telephone. She called Hatfield International. 'Good morning. This is Julia Baker. I'd like to speak to Miss Harper.'

She listened for a minute. 'I understand. Thank you.' She put down the telephone and walked to the window.

She said quietly, 'She didn't come to work this morning. Edward, she disappeared last night. First, my father – now Miss Harper. Edward! You don't think they–'

Edward went to Julia and put his arm round her. 'No. No, they didn't hurt Miss Harper. She's a clever girl. Perhaps she left the city. She's safe, I know it. Now come and sit down.'

Edward and Julia sat down. He took her hand.

'Julia, I want you to listen to me.'

'What can I do?' thought Julia. 'I have to listen to you,' she said.

'You have to work with me. Go to Hatfield's offices. Ask for other files, but not the Omega file. Then they'll feel happier. But you have to go back there. When they're not looking, you can get another copy of the Omega file.'

'Yes,' said Julia. 'I'll go now.'

'I'll call you every hour. I'll know then that you're OK. And don't worry. Nothing can happen to you. I'm here.'

Julia arrived at Hatfield International half an hour later. All morning she looked through files on workers. She looked at Miss Harper's file. Her family lived in Atlanta. 'Perhaps she went home to her parents. Yes. That's it,' she thought. 'She'll be all right. They can't do anything to her there.'

All morning Julia waited for the right time. She wanted to be alone in the office. The files for future projects were on a shelf near the door.

At one o'clock, Edward called for the third time.

'Meet me in ten minutes at the front door of the building,' he said. 'And please don't be late. It's very important.'

Ten minutes later, Julia was outside the front door. There were a lot of people in the street. It was nearly Christmas, and they looked happy and busy. Julia remembered last Christmas. She was with her father then, and . . .

Two very tall men came across the street. They had the long red coats of Father Christmas, and they called, 'Happy Christmas to you! Happy Christmas!'

Suddenly, they were next to her. They took her arms and pushed her across the street.

'What are you doing?' she shouted. 'Take your hands off me! No, no!'

A car door opened, and they pushed her inside. Strong arms took her arms. She fought them and hit her head on the car door. Her world started to go dark . . . She remembered one last thing. There was an arm round her. It was an arm in a green jacket.

'Edward West – Edward West is one of them!'

Chapter 8   Father and Daughter

Julia opened her eyes. The world went round and round. And there were noises in her head.

No. Not in her head. The noises were the sounds of an aeroplane. She was on a plane. Edward was next to her.

'Edward, weren't we friends?'

'Yes, we were. We are. I saved your life again.'

'Did you?'

'Yes. Mr Berger and his friends planned another little "accident" for you. I had to take you away from New York.'

'Where am I?'

'Now? We're flying over Florida.'

Julia looked round. 'But this – this is my father's plane. What are you doing with my father's plane?'

'It's a long story. Give me time and I'll tell you everything.'

'Start now.'

'First, a drink.'

'I don't want a drink. I want an answer.'

Edward smiled. 'That's the sad thing about rich girls. They always want everything now. Oh, OK.'

He started to tell her. Julia listened and watched his face.

'I wasn't wrong,' she thought. 'He's a good person.'

'I work for your father,' he said. 'After he disappeared, I watched you nearly every hour of every day. He was very worried about you. He wanted me to watch you, but he didn't want you to see me.'

'Where *is* my father?'

'I'll tell you that in a minute. First, you have to know something. Your father had to leave New York quickly. He learnt about Project Omega, and he wanted to stop his directors. They tried to kill him. He had to disappear.'

'My father knew about Project Omega? Why didn't he tell the world about it?'

'He couldn't. He didn't want to hurt the company – *your* company. "I can't do that to her," he told me. "She can finish the company. But not me." So you make your future – he doesn't make it.'

'What do you mean?'

'"Wait and help her when the time comes," he said to me. "When she learns about Project Omega."'

'OK. Perhaps I believe you. But where are you taking me?'

'To your father. He's waiting for you. Oh, and I found Miss Harper. She's safe. She's staying with her aunt outside Atlanta.'

'Oh, good. I was worried about her. She tried to help me.'

'And she's clever! She's got another copy of the Omega file!'

The plane came down to the ground. Edward opened the door

and jumped down. Julia followed him. It was hot, and she could see flowers and trees. They were a long way from winter in New York!

Then she saw him. A tall man with a lot of white hair. His face was brown from the sun.

'Dad!'

Later that evening, they sat in a garden and talked about the future.

'Julia, my dear, I don't want to go back to New York. I'd like to stay here in the sun,' said Charles Hatfield Baker III. 'I enjoy this life.'

Julia smiled at him, with love in her eyes. 'Perhaps when I'm seventy, I'll enjoy it with you. But now I've got an important job. Hatfield International is going to disappear, but there's a lot of money there. I want to use that money for good projects. I want to help people.'

She looked at Edward. Edward looked at her.

'I'd like to help you with that,' he said.

ACTIVITIES

Chapters 1–4

Before you read

1 Talk about the picture on pages 2 and 3. What can you see? Where and when does this story happen?

2 Read these sentences. What are the words in *italics* in your language? They are all in the story.

   a I'm *worried* about my little sister. She *disappeared* last night and we can't find her. Perhaps she's in *danger*. Perhaps somebody *kidnapped* her!

   b I've got three new jobs with *international* companies. Their *projects* are very big, so there's a lot of work. Look at those *files* on my desk.

   c He *owns* the company, and he's the only *director*. He has the *power*, and we have to listen to him. A lot of workers leave, and I'm not *surprised*.

   d You'll have to walk up to my flat. The *lift* isn't working.

   e I'm going to put this money in the *safe*. I don't *believe* that it will be *safe* in your bag!

   Now find the words in *italics* in your dictionary. Were you right?

After you read

3 Are these sentences about Julia right or wrong?

   a She lives in a flat in Manhattan.

   b She is worried about her father.

   c The directors of the company want to tell her everything.

   d She finds important papers in the Project Omega file.

   e Miss Harper wants to help her.

Chapters 5–8

Before you read

4 Julia thinks, 'What's happening? What's happening to Miss Harper? Does Project Omega mean danger for her too?' What do *you* think?

25

5 Answer the questions. Find the words in *italics* in your dictionary.

    a Are you *alone* when you are with a friend?

    b Is your teacher happy with a *copy* of another student's homework?

    c Do people *dream* when they are asleep?

    d Is an *evil* plan good?

    e Do people feel happy when they are *lonely*?

    f Do firemen want to *save* lives?

After you read

6 Why are these important in the story? Talk about them.

    a the Project Omega file

    b Miss Harper

    c the lift

7 How do these change in the story? Why are the changes important?

    a the weather

    b Julia's life

Writing

8 It is the day after Charles Hatfield Baker III disappears. Write the story for a newspaper. What happened?

9 Miss Harper is at her aunt's house. What did she know about Project Omega? Why did she leave New York? Will she come back? Write a letter from her to Julia.

10 At the end of the story, Edward West and Julia are talking about the future. What do they say next? Write their conversation.

11 It is a year later. What is Julia doing now? Write a letter from Julia to her father.